Contents

ISBN 0-86163-456-X

© Valerie Anne Limited 1984
Award Publications Limited 1984
Spring House, Spring Place
London NW5, England
Reprinted 1990

Printed in Malaysia

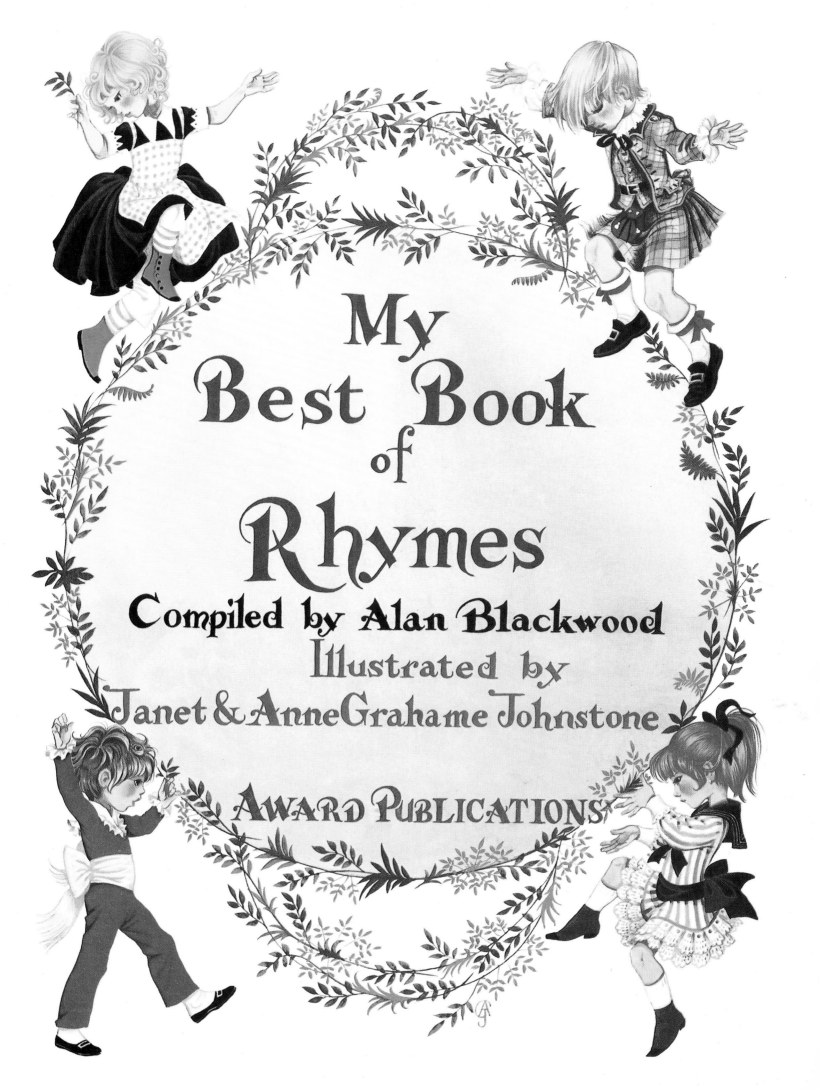

My Best Book of Rhymes

Compiled by Alan Blackwood

Illustrated by
Janet & Anne Grahame Johnstone

AWARD PUBLICATIONS

The Mulberry Bush

Here we go round the Mulberry Bush,
  the Mulberry Bush, the Mulberry Bush,
Here we go round the Mulberry Bush,
On a cold and frosty morning.

Who shall we send to fetch him out,
  fetch him out, fetch him out?
Who shall we send to fetch him out?
On a cold and frosty morning.

Pussy cat, Pussy cat

Pussy cat, pussy cat,
Where have you been?
I've been to London
To look at the Queen.
Pussy cat, pussy cat,
What did you there?
I frightened a little mouse under her chair.

Hey, diddle, diddle

Hey, diddle, diddle, the cat and the fiddle,
The cow jumped over the moon;
The little dog laughed to see such fun,
And the dish ran away with the spoon.

The Crooked Man

There was a crooked man,
And he walked a crooked mile,
He found a crooked sixpence
Against a crooked stile;
He bought a crooked cat,
Which caught a crooked mouse,
And they all lived together
In a little crooked house.

Mary had a Little Lamb

Mary had a little lamb,
Its fleece was white as snow;
And everywhere that Mary went
The lamb was sure to go.

It followed her to school one day,
That was against the rule;
It made the children laugh and play
To see a lamb at school.

Old King Cole

Old King Cole
Was a merry old soul,
And a merry old soul was he.
He called for his pipe,
And he called for his bowl,
And he called for his fiddlers three.

Daffy-Down-Dilly

Daffy-down-dilly is new come to town,
In a yellow petticoat, and a green gown.

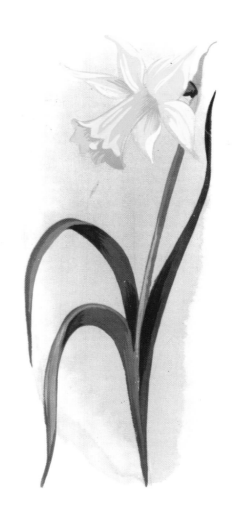

Rain

Rain, rain, go away,
Come again another day.

Humpty, Dumpty

Humpty Dumpty sat on a wall,
Humpty Dumpty had a great fall;
All the King's horses and all the King's men
Couldn't put Humpty together again.

Hickory, Dickory Dock

Hickory, dickory, dock,
The mouse ran up the clock.
The clock struck one,
The mouse ran down
Hickory, dickory, dock.

Cock-a-doodle doo

Cock a doodle doo!
My dame has lost her shoe,
My master's lost his fiddling stick,
And knows not what to do.

Jack be Nimble

Jack be nimble,
    Jack be quick,
Jack jump over
    The candlestick.

One, Two, Buckle my shoe

One, two,
Buckle my shoe;
Three, four,
Knock at the door;
Five, six,
Pick up sticks;
Seven, eight,
Lay them straight;
Nine, ten,
A big fat hen;
Eleven, twelve,
Dig and delve;
Thirteen, fourteen,
Maids a'courting;
Fifteen, sixteen,
Maids in the kitchen;
Seventeen, eighteen,
Maids a'waiting;
Nineteen, twenty,
My plate's empty.

Rock-a-bye Baby

Rock-a-bye baby
On a tree-top,
When the wind blows
The cradle will rock.

When the bough breaks
The cradle will fall,
Down will come baby,
Cradle and all.

Little Jack Horner

Little Jack Horner sat in the corner,
Eating a Christmas pie;
He put in his thumb,
And pulled out a plum,
And said, what a good boy am I!

Tom, Tom, the Piper's son

Tom, Tom, the piper's son,
Stole a pig and away he run;
The pig was eaten,
And Tom was beat,
And Tom went howling down the street.

Cross Patch

Cross patch,
Draw the latch,
Sit by the fire and spin;
Take a cup,
And drink it up,
Then call your neighbours in.

The North Wind Doth Blow

The North wind doth blow,
And we shall have snow,
And what will poor robin do then?
Poor thing!
He'll sit in a barn,
To keep himself warm,
And hide his head under his wing.
Poor thing!

Higgledy, Piggledy

Higgledy, Piggledy,
My black hen,
She lays eggs
For gentlemen;
Sometimes nine,
And sometimes ten,
Higgledy, Piggledy,
My black hen.

Sing a Song of Sixpence

Sing a song of sixpence,
A pocket full of rye;
Four and twenty blackbirds,
Baked in a pie.

When the pie was opened,
The birds began to sing;
Wasn't that a dainty dish
To set before the king?

The king was in his counting-house,
Counting out his money;
The queen was in the parlour,
Eating bread and honey.

The maid was in the garden,
Hanging out the clothes,
When down came a blackbird
And pecked off her nose.

They sent for the king's doctor,
Who sewed it on again,
And he sewed it on so neatly,
The seam was never seen.

Little Miss Muffet

Little Miss Muffet sat on a tuffet,
Eating her curds and whey;
There came a big spider,
Who sat down beside her
And frightened Miss Muffet away.

The Queen of Hearts

The Queen of Hearts
She made some tarts,
All on a summer's day;
The Knave of Hearts
He stole the tarts,
And took them clean away.

As I Was Going to St. Ives

As I was going to St. Ives
I met a man with seven wives;
Every wife had seven sacks,
Every sack had seven cats,
Every cat had seven kits.
Kits, cats, sacks and wives,
How many were there going to St. Ives?

The House that Jack Built

This is the farmer sowing his corn,
That kept the cock that crowed in the morn,
That waked the priest all shaven and shorn,
That married the man all tattered and torn,
That kissed the maiden all forlorn,
That milked the cow with the crumpled horn,
That tossed the dog,
That worried the cat,
That killed the rat,
That ate the malt
That lay in the house that Jack built.

Little Boy Blue

Little boy blue,
Come blow your horn,
The sheep's in the meadow,
The cow's in the corn.

Where is the boy
Who looks after the sheep?
He's under the haystack
Fast asleep.

Little Bo-Peep

Little Bo-Peep has lost her sheep,
And doesn't know where to find them;
Leave them alone and they'll come home,
Bringing their tails behind them.

Three Wise Men of Gotham

Three wise men of Gotham
Went to sea in a bowl:
And if the bowl had been stronger,
My song would have been longer.

Peter Piper

Peter Piper picked a peck of pickled pepper;
A peck of pickled pepper Peter Piper picked;
If Peter Piper picked a peck of pickled pepper,
Where's the peck of pickled pepper Peter Piper picked?

Monday's child is fair of face,

Tuesday's child is full of grace,

Wednesday's child is full of woe,

Thursday's child has far to go,

37

FRIDAY

Friday's child is loving and giving,

ONIONS

Saturday's child works hard for its living,

And the child that's born on the Sabbath day,

Is fair and wise and good and gay.

Cobbler, Cobbler

Cobbler, cobbler, mend my shoe,
Get it done by half past two;
Stitch it up, and stitch it down,
Then I'll give you half a crown.

Polly Flinders

Little Polly Flinders
Sat among the cinders,
Warming her pretty little toes;
Her mother came and caught her,
And whipped her little daughter
For spoiling her nice new clothes.

Oranges and Lemons

Oranges and Lemons
Say the bells of St. Clement's
I owe you five farthings
Say the bells of St. Martin's
When will you pay me?
Say the bells of Old Bailey.
When I grow rich,
Say the bells of Shoreditch
When will that be?
Say the bells of Stepney
I do not know
Says the great bell of Bow.

Solomon Grundy

Solomon Grundy,
Born on a Monday,
Christened on Tuesday,
Married on Wednesday,
Took ill on Thursday,
Worse on Friday,
Died on Saturday,
Buried on Sunday:
This is the end
Of Solomon Grundy.

Baa, Baa, Black Sheep

Baa, baa, black sheep
Have you any wool?
Yes, sir, yes, sir,
Three bags full:
One for the master,
And one for the dame,
And one for the little boy
Who lives down the lane.

Three Blind Mice

Three blind mice,
See how they run!
They all ran after the farmer's wife,
Who cut off their tails with a carving-knife,
Did you ever see such a thing in your life?
As three blind mice.

Please to Remember

Please to remember
The fifth of November
Gunpowder treason and plot ;
We know no reason
Why gunpowder treason
Should ever be forgot.

The Man in the Wilderness

The man in the wilderness asked of me
How many strawberries grew in the sea.
I answered him as I thought good,
As many as red herrings grow in the wood.

A Frog He Would A-Wooing Go

A frog he would a-wooing go,
Heigh ho! says Rowley.
Whether his mother would let him or no:
With a rowley-powley, gammon and spinach.
Heigh ho! says Anthony Rowley.

So off he set in his opera-hat,
Heigh ho! says Rowley.
And on his way he met with a Rat.
With a rowley-powley, gammon and spinach.
Heigh ho! says Anthony Rowley.

Pray, Mr. Rat, will you go with me?
Heigh ho! says Rowley.
Pretty Miss Mousey for to see?
With a rowley-powley, gammon and spinach.
Heigh ho! says Anthony Rowley.

They soon arrived at Mousey Hall,
Heigh ho! says Rowley.
They gave a loud knock and gave a loud call.
With a rowley-powley, gammon and spinach.
Heigh ho! says Anthony Rowley.

Pray, Miss Mousey, are you within.
Heigh ho! says Rowley.
Oh, yes, kind sirs. I'm sitting to spin.
With a rowley-powley, gammon and spinach.
Heigh ho! says Anthony Rowley

Four and Twenty Tailors

Four and twenty tailors went to kill a snail,
The best man amongst them durst not touch her tail
She put out her horns like a little Kyloe cow,
Run, tailors, run or she'll kill you all e'en now!

Jack Sprat

Jack Sprat could eat no fat,
His wife could eat no lean;
So it came to pass, between them both,
They licked the platter clean.

Jack ate all the lean,
Joan ate all the fat,
The bone they picked it clean,
Then gave it to the cat.

The Little Nut Tree

I had a little nut tree,
Nothing would it bear
But a silver nutmeg
And a golden pear;
The King of Spain's daughter
Came to visit me,
And all for the sake of my little nut tree.

Georgie Porgie

Georgie Porgie, pudding and pie,
Kissed the girls and made them cry;
When the boys came out to play,
Georgie Porgie ran away.

Tom He Was a Piper's Son

Tom he was a piper's son,
He learnt to play when he was young;
But all the tunes that he could play
Was "Over the hills and far away."
Over the hills and a great way off,
The wind shall blow my top-knot off.

Tom with his pipe made such a noise
That he pleased both the girls and boys.
And they stopped to hear him play
"Over the hills and far away."
Over the hills and a great way off,
The wind shall blow my top-knot off.

Tom played his pipe with such a skill
Those who heard him could never keep still;
Whenever they heard they had to dance,
Even the pigs would after him prance.
Over the hills and a great way off,
The wind shall blow my top-knot off.

Ladybird, Ladybird

Ladybird, ladybird,
Fly away home,
Your house is on fire
And your children all gone;
All except one
And that's little Ann
And she crept under
The warming pan.

Who Killed
Cock Robin?

Who killed Cock Robin?
I, said the Sparrow,
With my bow and arrow,
I killed Cock Robin.

Who saw him die?
I, said the Magpie,
With my little eye,
I saw him die.

Who'll be the parson?
I said the Rook,
With my little book,
I'll be the parson.

Who'll be chief mourner?
I, said the Swan,
I'm sorry he's gone,
I'll be chief mourner.

Who'll toll the bell?
I said the Bull,
Because I can pull,
And I'll toll the bell.

Tell Tale Tit

Tell tale, tit!
Your tongue shall be split,
And all the dogs in the town
Shall have a little bit.

Thirty Days Hath September

Thirty days hath September,
April, June, and November;
All the rest have thirty-one,
Excepting February alone,
And that has twenty-eight days clear
And twenty-nine in each leap year.

My Pretty Maid

Where are you going to, my pretty maid?
Where are you going to, my pretty maid?
I'm going a-milking, Sir, she said,
Sir, she said, Sir, she said,
I'm going a-milking, Sir, she said.

Shall I go with you, my pretty maid?
Shall I go with you, my pretty maid?
Yes, if you please, kind Sir, she said,
Sir, she said, Sir, she said,
Yes, if you please, kind Sir, she said.

What is your fortune, my pretty maid?
What is your fortune, my pretty maid?
My face is my fortune, Sir, she said,
Sir, she said, Sir, she said,
My face is my fortune, Sir, she said.

        Then I can't marry you, my pretty maid!
        Then I can't marry you, my pretty maid!
        And nobody asked you, Sir! she said,
        Sir, she said, Sir, she said,
        And nobody asked you, Sir, she said.

The King of France

The King of France went up the hill,
With twenty thousand men;
The King of France came down the hill,
And ne'er went up again.

If I Had as Much Money

If I had as much money as I could spend
I never would cry, "Old chairs to mend;
Old chairs to mend, old chairs to mend;"
I never would cry, "Old chairs to mend."

If I had as much money as I could tell
I never would cry, "Old clothes to sell;
Old clothes to sell, old clothes to sell;"
I never would cry, "Old clothes to sell!"

This Little Pig

This little pig went to market;
This little pig stayed at home;
This little pig had roast beef;
And this little pig had none;
And this little pig cried, "Wee, wee wee!
I can't find my way home."

Old Mother Hubbard

Old Mother Hubbard
Went to the cupboard,
To get her poor dog a bone;
But when she got there
The cupboard was bare,
And so the poor dog had none.

a Penny, Two a Penny

One a penny, two a penny,
Hot cross buns;
If your daughters do not like them,
Give them to your sons.

Pat-a-cake

Pat-a-cake, pat-a-cake, baker's man,
Bake me a cake as fast as you can;
Pat it and prick it, and mark it with B,
Put it in the oven for Baby and me.

Goosey Goosey Gander

Goosey goosey gander,
Whither shall I wander?
Upstairs and downstairs,
And in my lady's chamber;
There I met an old man
Who would not say his prayers;
I took him by the left leg,
And threw him down the stairs.

The Lion and the Unicorn

The lion and the unicorn
Were fighting for the crown;
The lion beat the unicorn
All around the town.
Some gave them white bread,
And some gave them brown;
Some gave them plum cake,
And sent them out of town.

Boys and Girls come out to play

Boys and girls come out to play,
The moon doth shine as bright as day.
Leave your supper and leave your sleep,
And join your friends out in the street.
Come with a whoop and come with a call,
Come with a goodwill or not at all.
Up the ladder and down the wall,
A half-penny loaf will serve us all;
You find milk, and I'll find flour,
And we'll have a pudding in half an hour.

Ding Dong Bell

Ding dong bell,
Pussy's in the well:
Who put her in?
Little Tommy Thin.
Who pulled her out?
Little Tommy Stout?
What a naughty boy was that
To drown poor pussy cat.
Who ne'er did any harm,
But killed all the mice in Father's barn.

I Love Little Pussy

I love little pussy,
Her coat is so warm,
And if I don't hurt her,
She'll do me no harm.
So I'll not pull her tail,
Or drive her away,
But pussy and I
Very gently will play.
She will sit by my side,
And I'll give her her food,
And she'll like me because
I am gentle and good.

Mary, Mary, Quite Contrary

Mary, Mary, quite contrary,
How does your garden grow?
With silver bells and cockle shells,
And pretty maids all in a row.

Ring-a-ring o' Roses

Ring-a-ring o' roses,
A pocket full of posies,
A-tishoo! A-tishoo!
We all fall down.

Diddle, Diddle, Dumpling

Diddle, diddle, dumpling, my son John
Went to bed with his trousers on;
One shoe off, and one shoe on,
Diddle, diddle, dumpling, my son John.

There was a Little Girl

There was a little girl, and she had a little curl
Right in the middle of her forehead;
When she was good she was very, very good,
But when she was bad she was horrid.

Curly Locks

Curly locks, Curly locks, wilt thou be mine?
Thou shalt not wash dishes, nor yet feed the swine;
But sit on a cushion and sew a fine seam,
And feed upon strawberries, sugar and cream.

Tommy Tucker

Little Tommy Tucker sings for his supper:
What shall we give him?
White bread and butter.
How shall he cut it without a knife?
How will he marry without a wife?

Pease Porridge

Pease-porridge hot, pease-porridge cold,
Pease-porridge in the pot, nine days old.

Polly put the Kettle on

Polly put the kettle on,
Polly put the kettle on,
Polly put the kettle on,
We'll all have tea.

Sukey take it off again,
Sukey take it off again,
Sukey take it off again,
They've all gone away.

See-saw Margery Daw

See-saw, Margery Daw,
Jack shall have a new master;
Jack shall have but a penny a day,
Because he can't work any faster.

What are Little Boys made of?

What are little boys made of, made of?
What are little boys made of?
Snips and snails,
And puppy-dogs tails,
That's what little boys are made of.

What are little girls made of, made of?
What are little girls made of?
Sugar and spice
And all things nice,
That's what little girls are made of.

Bye, Baby Bunting

Bye, baby bunting,
Daddy's gone a-hunting,
Gone to get a rabbit skin
To wrap the baby bunting in.

Simple Simon

Simple Simon met a pieman,
Going to the fair;
Says Simple Simon to the pieman,
Let me taste your ware.
Says the pieman to Simple Simon,
Show me first your penny;
Says Simple Simon to the pieman,
Indeed I have not any.

Ride a cock-horse

Ride a cock-horse to Banbury Cross,
To see a fine lady upon a white horse;
Rings on her fingers and bells on her toes,
She shall have music wherever she goes.

To bed, to bed

"To bed, to bed" said Sleepy Head,
"Tarry a while" said Slow,
"Put on the pan" said Greedy Ann,
"We'll sup before we go"

How Many Miles to Babylon?

How many miles to Babylon?
Three score miles and ten.
Can I get there by candle-light?
Yes, and back again.
If your heels are nimble and light,
You may get there by candle-light.

Twinkle, twinkle, little Star

Twinkle, twinkle, little star,
How I wonder what you are!
Up above the world so high,
Like a diamond in the sky.

Wee Willie Winkie

Wee Willie Winkie runs through the town,
Upstairs and downstairs in his night-gown,
Rapping at the window, crying through the lock,
Are the children all in bed, for now it's eight o'clock.